CW00391997

Contents

? Shows pages with puzzles and theory questions

Revision of Scales

A **scale** is the stepwise progression of notes in alphabetical order from any note to its octave. There are many different kinds of scales. The most commonly used one is the **major scale**. This scale can be sung using tonic sol-fa:

Doh - Re - Mi - Fa - Soh - La - Ti - Doh.

C Major: no key signature because it has no sharps (using only the white notes on a keyboard).

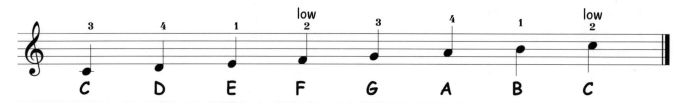

G Major: lower octave: the key signature has one sharp, F♯.

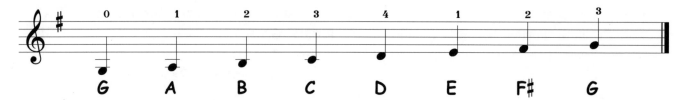

G Major: upper octave

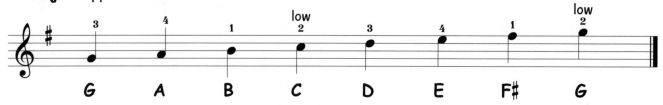

D Major: the key signature has two sharps, F♯ and C♯.

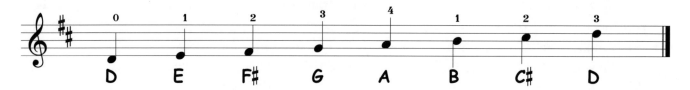

The Arpeggio

The **arpeggio** is built from the most important notes of the scale. They are the 1st, 3rd, 5th and 8th notes. Here is the **D major** arpeggio.

Can you work out the arpeggios for the other keys?
Start on the key note (the first note of the scale).

Bow Tricks: Bowing Variations

A **study** is a piece of music intended to improve a particular skill or 'trick'.

A **variation** is the same melody played in a different way.

First learn to play the theme from memory.

Then play the same tune using the different bowing patterns below.

Study in D

A. Akerman

The Italian word **staccato** means 'cut short'.
It is indicated by a dot placed over or under a note
to show that it is to be played short and detached.
Stop the bow between notes.

Rigaudon

A **rigaudon** is a lively dance from the Provencal region of France. It first became
popular at the court of King Louis XIII in the 1630s and in England, around 1700.

4

Bar numbers are placed at the beginning of each line to help you find your place easily in longer pieces of music.

Henry Purcell (1659-1695) was an English composer. As a boy he was a chorister with the Chapel Royal. He was the organist at Westminster Abbey and Keeper of the Royal Instruments. Later he became the King's Composer.

Rigaudon

Harmony Part

Purcell
arr. A. Akerman

? Music signs

1. Join each music sign to its correct term.

Treble clef
Minim
Time signature for four beats
Natural
Whole bar rest
Stave, staff
Gradually louder
Sharp
Very soft
Up bow
Quaver
Crotchet rest
Moderately loud
Down bow
Repeat
Slur

2. There are seven mistakes in this music.
   Rewrite the music correctly on the stave below.

Faster Rhythms: Semiquavers

 This note is a semiquaver.
It is worth a quarter of a crotchet.

kook-a-bur-ra

Bow the 'kookaburra' rhythm on an open string.
Now play the scale of G major with four semiquavers on each note.

Hornpipe

A **hornpipe** is a lively English dance from the 18th century. It was accompanied by an instrument of the same name, a wooden pipe made with a single reed attached at one end and an animal's horn at the other. The hornpipe became a traditional dance of sailors, perhaps because it could be danced solo in a small space.

7

Often two semiquavers are joined to a quaver to make another kind of rhythmic pattern.

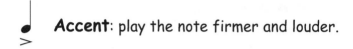

grass-hop-per

Bow this rhythm on an open string.
Play the scale of the tune below using this rhythm on each note.

Accent: play the note firmer and louder.

Fiddle Music: Three Reels

Fiddle music is the traditional folk and dance music of many countries. There are many variations of these tunes and many have more than one name because they are usually passed on from one generation to another by ear, the learner listening and copying them.

A **reel** is quick, lively dance. It is usually danced in groups of four with two couples facing each other.

These three reels may be played as separate short tunes or as a single continuous piece.

The Rakes of Mallow

Irish Reel

A quaver may be joined to two semiquavers in this way.

hop-per-grass
(grasshopper backwards!)

Carl Maria von Weber
(1786-1826) was a German pianist, conductor and composer. He is best known for his operas, which are full of romance and mystery.

Hunters' Chorus

Allegro

Weber

10

Key Signatures

?

1. Key signatures are always written with F♯ on the fifth line and C♯ in the third space. Copy these key signatures placing the sharps correctly.

G Major has 1 sharp: F♯.

D Major has 2 sharps: F♯ and C♯.

C Major has no sharps so no key signature.

2. Write the following notes.

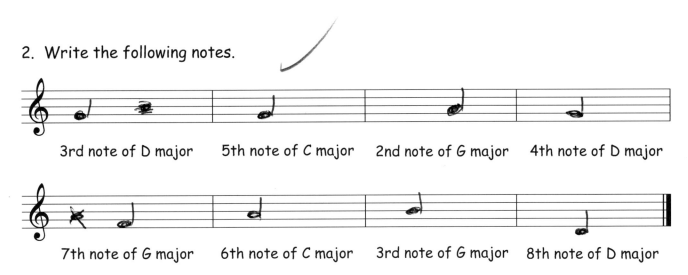

3rd note of D major   5th note of C major   2nd note of G major   4th note of D major

7th note of G major   6th note of C major   3rd note of G major   8th note of D major

3. This melody should be in the scale of D major but the key signature has been left out. Put a sharp sign in front of each note that needs it.

4. Continue writing the following notes in two different places on the staff, one low and the other an octave higher.

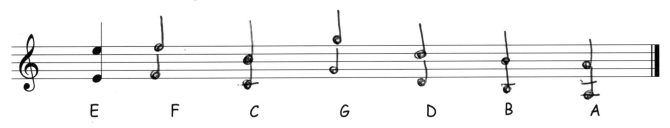

E   F   C   G   D   B   A

11

The Relative Value of Notes and Rests

Notes

A semibreve
is equal in value
to   **2 minims**

or   **4 crotchets**

or   **8 quavers**

or **16 semiquavers**

Notes can also be named according to their comparative value.

A **semibreve** 𝗈 is also called a whole note.

A **minim** is a $\frac{1}{2}$ (half) note.

A **crotchet** is a $\frac{1}{4}$ (quarter) note.

A **quaver** is a $\frac{1}{8}$ (eighth) note.

A **semiquaver** is a $\frac{1}{16}$ (sixteenth) note.

A dot placed after a note makes it half as long again, the dot being worth half the value of the note.

12

Rests

Music has silences as well as sounds.
Every note has a corresponding rest of the same value to represent silence.

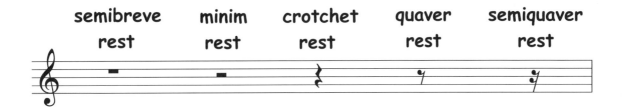

Silence for an entire bar is always indicated by a semibreve rest no matter what the time signature is. This is why its other name is a whole bar rest.

A rest of several bars in length is shown by placing a number over a single bar.

Grouping

Notes and rests are always grouped together in beats according to the time signature.

Correct

Incorrect

Finger Tricks: Fourth Finger Power

Are you like many young violinists who find using the fourth finger difficult?
Maybe you are forgetting to hold your left hand correctly.
Here is an exercise or 'trick' to help your smallest finger improve its performance.
Play this exercise daily and soon you will find it easy.
Remember to listen very carefully to keep the notes in tune.

Also try the same finger patterns on the other strings.

Variation: play the same notes and finger patterns slurring with one bow per bar.

Bowing Tricks: String Changing

Play the above exercise and variation again, this time using an open string.
Change strings with a relaxed hand and forearm.
Keep your left hand fingers on the string, well curved and standing on their tips,
while playing the open string under them.

14

Legato: play smoothly.
It is the opposite of staccato.

Antonin Dvorak (1841-1904) was a viola player and a famous Czech composer. While working in America for three years, he was influenced by African-American music, as in this melody, part of a large piece of orchestral music called a **symphony**.

Theme from the 'New World' Symphony

(Use your fourth finger wherever possible.)

Dvorak

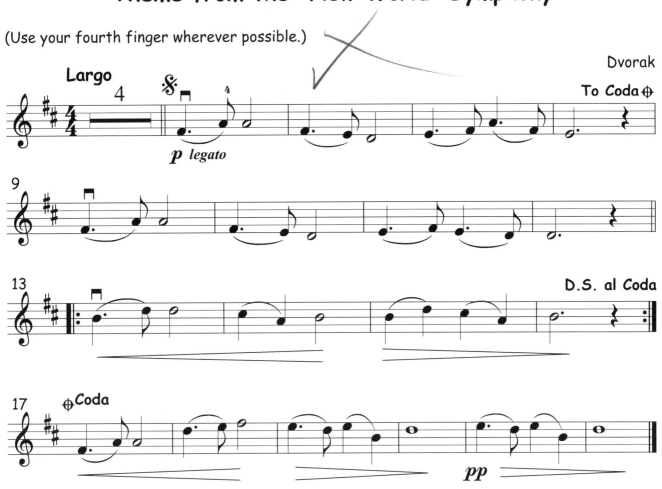

S. stands for the Italian word **segno** which means a **sign**: 𝄋 or ⊕
The **Coda** is the 'tail' or ending.
D.S. al Coda means go back to 𝄋 and play from there until **To Coda** ⊕
then skip to ⊕**Coda** to finish the piece.

To play this piece: play line 1, line 2, line 3 twice,
line 1 again without the 4 bars introduction
then line 4.

15

A **triplet** is a group of three notes played in the same time as two notes of the same kind. Each quaver in this triplet is worth one-third of a crotchet beat.

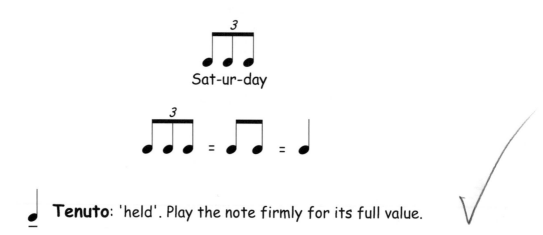

Sat-ur-day

♩ **Tenuto**: 'held'. Play the note firmly for its full value.

Irish Folk Song

Note Values

1. Write one note equal in value to each of the following bars.

2. Put the bar lines in each tune. Can you work out which one has an anacrusis (upbeat)?

3. Put the correct time signature in each of these bars.

4. Circle the notes that go together to make each crotchet beat.
   Then copy the notes onto the empty stave, grouping them correctly.

A **minuet** is a stately dance that was very popular in the royal courts of Europe in the 17th and 18th centuries. The minuet has a three-beat rhythm and is played and danced at a dignified tempo. This minuet has contrasting staccato and legato phrases.

James Hook (1746-1827) was an English composer who worked as an organist in London. He wrote over two thousand songs and many other short pieces of music.

Minuet

Hook

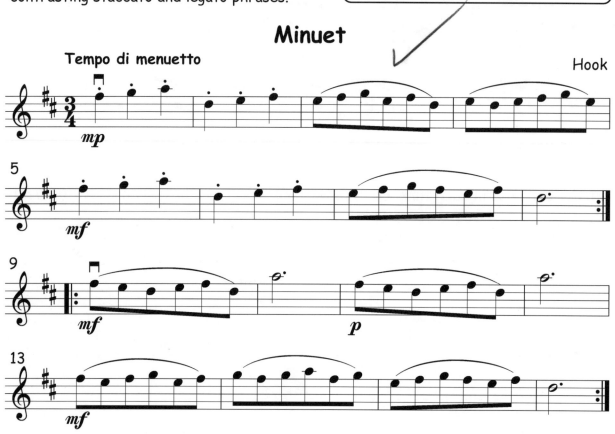

Harmony Part

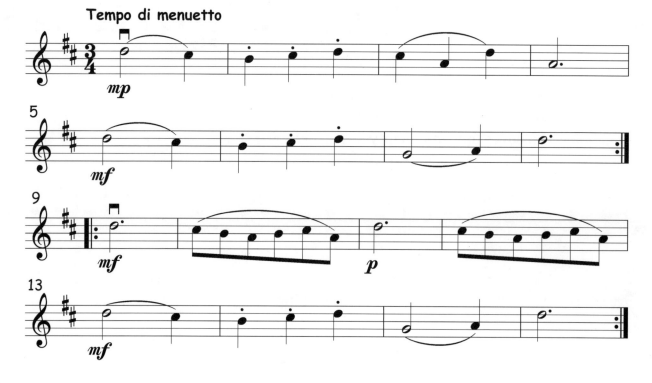

A New Note: B♭

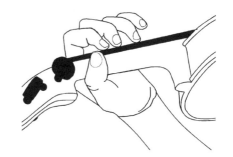

♭   This sign is called a **flat**.
It lowers a note by one semitone.
(It is the opposite of a sharp.)

To play B♭ on the G string place your
second finger in the low 2 position.

Snake in the Grass

Andante

Traditional

B♭ is halfway between A and B.

To play B♭ on the A string,
stretch your first finger back
and place it between the open
string and the normal first
finger position. Only move your
finger, not your whole hand.

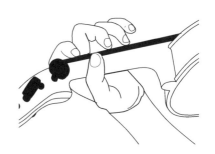

Finger Tricks: low first finger

Hot cross ♭uns

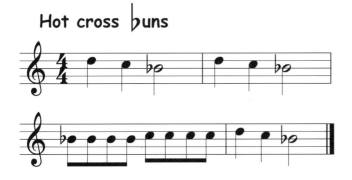

When you reach back with your first
finger, make sure your other fingers
stay in their correct places. Listen
carefully to keep in tune.

Tones and Semitones

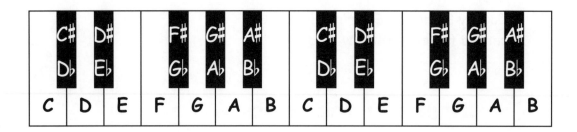

These are the notes of a music keyboard such as a piano. We can recognise each note by the way the black notes are grouped in twos and threes. The white notes are named after the first seven letters of the alphabet. The black notes are named after the letter name of the nearest white note, either sharp (higher) or flat (lower). So B flat can also be called A sharp. Notes that have the same pitch but different names are called **enharmonic notes**.

There is no black note between **E and F** or between **B and C**.

A **semitone** is the distance from any note to the one immediately above or below it counting all notes, both black and white.

e.g.　　**C to C♯**　　**B♭ to B**　　**E to F**

A **tone** is two semitones.

e.g.　　**C to D**　　**A♭ to B♭**　　**E to F♯**

Tones and Semitones (continued)

1. Write the enharmonic of these notes (different name, same pitch). The first one is done for you. Use the picture of the keyboard on the previous page to help you.

2. Write the note that is one semitone lower than each of these notes.

3. Write the note that is one tone higher than each of these notes.

4. Name the distance between each pair of notes, a tone (T) or a semitone (S).

21

B♭ Blues

Blues is a style of jazz music that was developed about 100 years ago by African-American musicians. The flattened 3rd note of the scale (B flat in the scale of G), is a feature of this style and is known as a 'blue' note.

♮ The natural sign cancels a ♯ or ♭ and returns the note to its natural position.

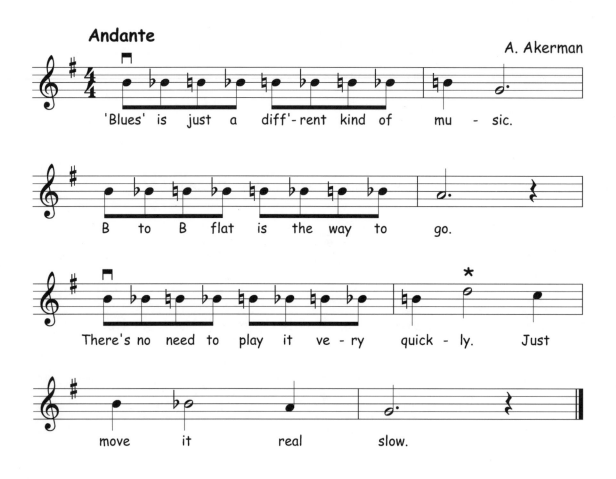

'Blues' is just a diff'-rent kind of mu - sic.

B to B flat is the way to go.

There's no need to play it ve - ry quick - ly. Just

move it real slow.

Challenge: Try to play this tune while keeping your third finger on the note G on the D string until the note marked *.

When a sharp, a flat or a natural is used to alter the pitch of a note, it is called an **accidental**. An accidental affects a note only until the next bar line.

Did you know?
The word **jazz** comes from the French word 'jaser' which means to gossip or chat together.

A 'Twinkle' Challenge

Part 1

If you used the earlier 'Tricks to Tunes' books you will already have learned to play the tune of 'Twinkle, Twinkle Little Star' beginning on an open string (in the key of D major), and on your 3rd finger (in C major).

Can you play the same tune starting on the note F?

Part 2

Write the tune of 'Twinkle' below starting on F.
The first bar has been written to help you.

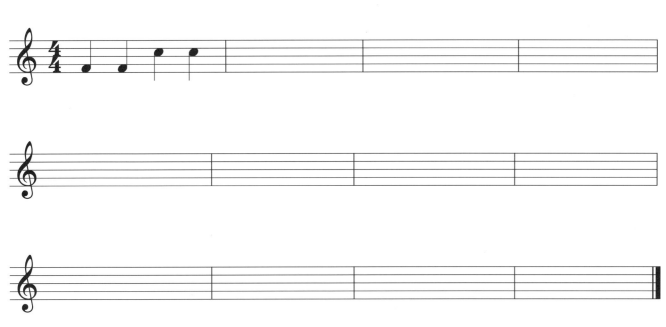

The Major Scale

All major scales have this pattern of tones and semitones.

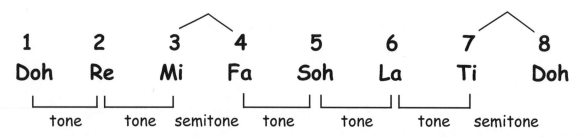

If you start on any note and play this order of steps (tones and semitones) in alphabetical order, you will get a major scale. The semitones always occur between the **3rd and 4th** notes and the **7th and 8th** notes. Try it for yourself.

F Major Scale

F major scale has one flat: B♭.

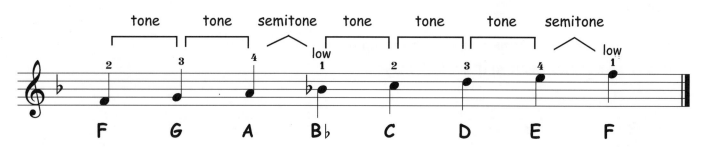

F natural on the E string is played with a low first finger, as there is only a semitone between E and F.

F Major Arpeggio

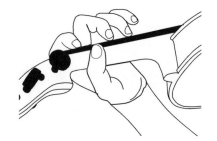

24

Tyrolean Dance

This is a traditional folk dance from the Tyrol Mountains in Austria.

Moderato

Spot the Difference

?

There are eight differences between each version of the music below.
Can you find them? Put a circle round each one.

This well-known Irish melody is also known as 'Danny Boy'. It first appeared in George Petrie's collection of 1855. It was given to Petrie by Jane Ross, who used to collect and write down tunes sung by the peasants who came to the town onf Limavady on market day.

Remember: when you play music in F major, play F (low 1st finger) on E string,
B♭ (low first finger) on A string and E (normal 1st finger) on D string.

The Londonderry Air

Scales and Intervals

1. Write the scale of F major using the key signature.
   Mark the semitones with slurs.

2. Write the following notes.

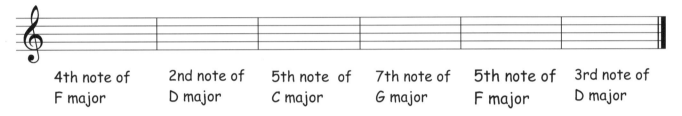

| 4th note of F major | 2nd note of D major | 5th note of C major | 7th note of G major | 5th note of F major | 3rd note of D major |

An **interval** is the distance between two notes. For example, the distance
from the first note to the third note of a scale is called the interval of a 3rd.
In the major scale 2nds, 3rds, 6ths and 7ths are called **major** intervals.
The 4ths, 5ths and octaves are called **perfect** intervals.

3. Above each of these notes write another to make the correct interval.
   The first has been done to show you how. Remember the given note is
   the first note of a major scale.

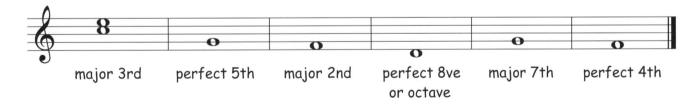

| major 3rd | perfect 5th | major 2nd | perfect 8ve or octave | major 7th | perfect 4th |

4. Name the following intervals.

A **nocturne** is a peaceful piece of music suggesting the quiet of the night. The title was first used by an Irish composer, John Field, who wrote many beautiful nocturnes for the piano.

Felix Mendelssohn (1809-1847) was a German composer, pianist and conductor who wrote this piece of 'night music'. It was inspired by **William Shakespeare's** play 'A Midsummer Night's Dream'.

Nocturne
(from 'A Midsummer Night's Dream')

? Find the Words

Staccato   Clef
Rhythm   Tie
Legato   Beat
Minuet   Bow
Reel   Rest
Tempo

```
P R H Y T H M L
B E A T E T I E
R E S T M I N G
C L E F P V U A
L E L B O W E T
S T A C C A T O
```

28

Time Signatures

Time in music is the grouping of strong and weaker beats into bars.

The **time signature** consists of two numbers.

The **top** number tells **how many** beats are in each bar.

The **bottom** number tells **what kind** of beat.

It is written at the beginning of the music, after the clef and key signature.

Simple Time

$\frac{2}{4}$ means 2 X $\frac{1}{4}$ that is, two crotchet (quarter note) beats in each bar.

$\frac{3}{4}$ means 3 X $\frac{1}{4}$ that is, three crotchet (quarter note) beats in each bar.

$\frac{4}{4}$ means 4 X $\frac{1}{4}$ that is, four crotchet (quarter note) beats in each bar.

$\frac{4}{4}$ is also called **common time** and is shown by the letter $\mathbb{C}$ instead of numbers.

2 beats in the bar is called **simple duple** time.

3 beats in the bar is called **simple triple** time.

4 beats in the bar is called **simple quadruple** time.

Compound Time

$\frac{6}{8}$ means 6 X $\frac{1}{8}$ that is, six quavers (eighth notes) in each bar.

In the **simple time** signatures above, the beat is a plain note (eg ♩)
and can be divided into two.

In **compound time** the main beat is a dotted note (eg ♩.)
and can be divided into three.

$\frac{6}{8}$ is called compound duple time because it has 2 dotted crotchet beats,
each divided into three quavers.

Fiddle Music: A Pair of Jigs

A **jig** is a lively dance in 6/8 that originated in Britain around 1600.
Jigs have continued to be a favourite up to the present time.

The Emerald Isle

Time Values and Signatures

1. Add a time signature to each bar.

2. Beside each note write a rest of the same value.

3. Complete these bars with rests. Finish an incomplete beat before completing the bar.

4. Beside each group of notes write one note of the same value.

5. Put a time signature in each bar as described.

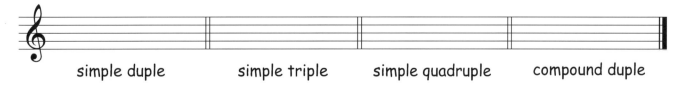

    simple duple   simple triple   simple quadruple   compound duple

Ornaments are used to decorate a melody.

Acciaccatura: (bars 5 & 19) This is a 'crushed' note or grace note. Play the small note as quickly as possible before the main note.

Mordent: (bars 6 & 20) Play the given note, the note above and then the given note again. Do this quickly, all in the one bow.

Soeur Monique

Couperin
Adapt. A. A.

The **Couperin** family were renowned French musicians. The best known was **François** (1668-1733). He became the organist in King Louis XIV's chapel at Versailles. He was especially famous for his books of harpsichord music from which this piece is taken.

For many years this music was thought to have been written by one of the world's greatest composers, **Wolfgang Amadeus Mozart**. It was in fact written by **Bernhard Flies** (born in Berlin around 1770) who was his contemporary. Flies published this music in 1795, four years after Mozart died. He probably sold many more copies by attributing it to this famous musician. The music is also known by its German name of 'Wiegenlied'.

Cradle Song

Andante tranquillo

Flies

Pizz. is short for **pizzicato**, which means plucked. Keep your bow hold but extend your first finger ready to play pizzicato. Pluck the string over the fingerboard, not where you bow.

The **harpsichord** is a keyboard instrument with strings that are plucked, rather than struck with a hammer like the piano. It was a common household instrument for many years before the invention of the piano in the latter half of the eighteenth century.

33

Bow Tricks: Bowing Variations

Study in F

Although **Italian** is the language generally used in music, **French** is the language most commonly used to describe the different types of bow stroke.

Détaché: detached
Change bow with every note, keeping the bow on the string.

A. Akerman

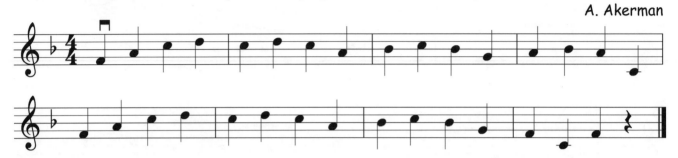

Variations

Martelé: 'hammered'
Use the upper part of the bow. Play each note as a strong, longer staccato with a bite at the beginning.

1

Hook stroke with repeated notes
This is like stopped slurs but with the first note long and strong for 3/4 of the beat, and the second note short and light for 1/4 of the beat.

2a

Hook stroke with changing notes

2b

34

This march has been arranged as a duet. To play the melody read
the notes on the upper stave. The harmony is on the lower stave.

tr The **trill** or shake is another ornament. Play the given note and the
one above it alternately and rapidly for the duration of the note.

March

This march is also known as 'Trumpet Tune' as it was originally written for that instrument.

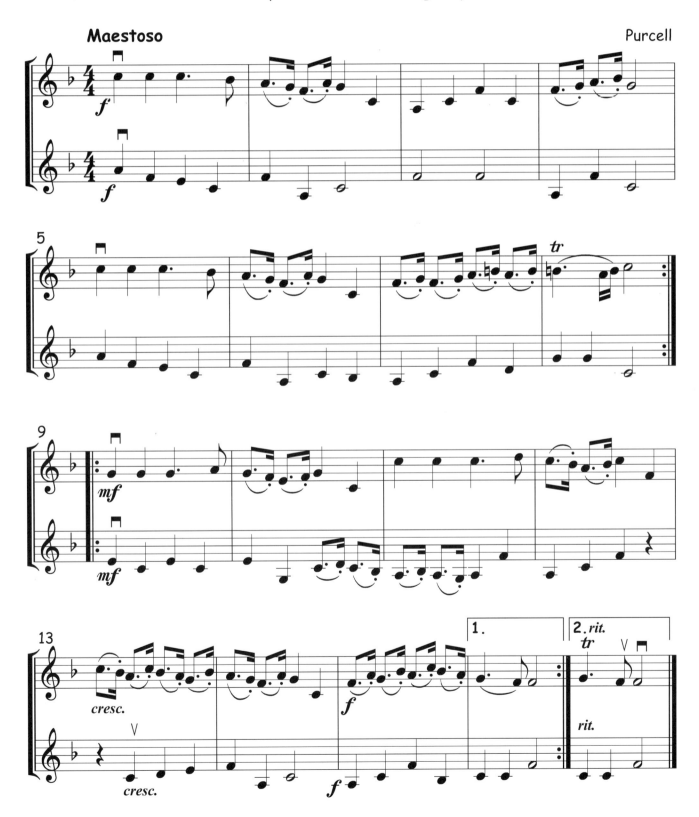

? Review

1. Write a note that is one semitone higher than each of these notes.

2. Put the time signatures and bar lines into these melodies.
   (a) 4 crotchets in each bar

   (b) 3 crotchets in each bar

3. Name the key of each tune above.

   (a)...

   (b)...

4. Add signs to the following melody to show that:
   (a) It is in the key of D major.
   (b) It is in common time.
   (c) It begins very softly.
   (d) Bars 3 and 4 gradually get louder.
   (e) The quavers in bar 2 are to be played staccato.
   (f) There is a fermata (pause) on the last note.
   (g) The melody is to be played twice.

Minor Scales

Like the major scale, the **minor scale** has 8 notes going in alphabetical order from any note to its octave. However, the minor scale has a different pattern of tones and semitones. This gives the minor scale a sad sound compared with the happy sound of the major scale. The **harmonic minor scale** is one kind of minor scale.

**To turn a major scale into a harmonic minor scale you
must lower the 3rd and 6th notes by one semitone.**

Here is the scale of **D major**.

Lower the 3rd note F♯ to F♮ and the 6th note B to B♭ to make the scale of **D minor**.

D minor has the same key signature as F major: B♭.
Scales with the same key signature are called related scales.
D minor is the relative minor of F major.
D minor has a C♯ which is not part of the key signature but is an accidental.
(Sharps and flats can't both be in a key signature.)

Play these scales and listen to the difference.
The position of the semitones is marked: ⌒

F major

D minor

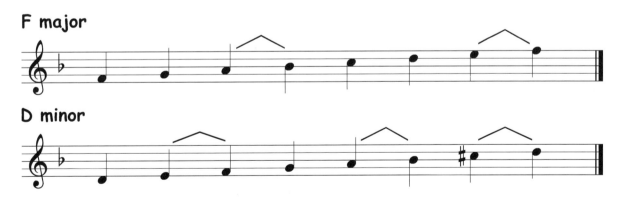

D minor arpeggio: compare it with the **D major arpeggio**.

37

A New Time Signature

Note this tune's time signature.

$\mathbf{C}$ Common time is the same as 4/4 with 4 crotchets in each bar.

$\mathcal{C}$ Alla breve or 'cut' time is the same as 2/2. Like $\mathbf{C}$ it has 4 crotchets in each bar but the beat is counted as 2 minims in each bar. This tends to make the music go faster.

Hatikvah

Traditional Hebrew
National Anthem of Israel

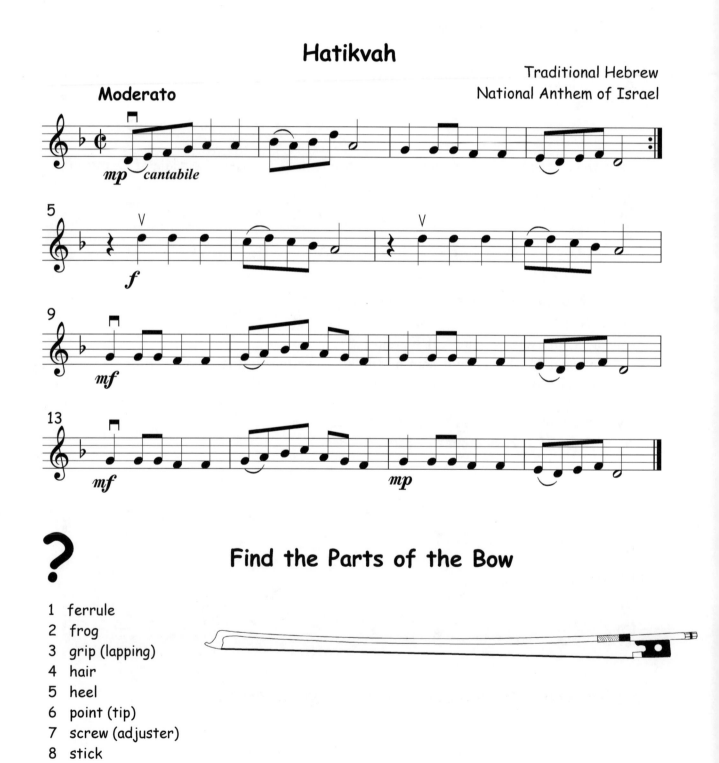

? Find the Parts of the Bow

1 ferrule
2 frog
3 grip (lapping)
4 hair
5 heel
6 point (tip)
7 screw (adjuster)
8 stick

Felix Mendelssohn was the son of a wealthy banker. He spent a lot of time travelling in Europe. Instead of writing postcards home to his family, he wrote music to describe the sights and sounds of his travels. This part of his 'Italian' Symphony was inspired by a religious procession that he saw when visiting Naples.

Theme from the 'Italian' Symphony

The Pilgrims' March

Find the Violin Parts

1 adjusters (fine tuners)
2 bridge
3 chin rest
4 f hole
5 fingerboard
6 neck
7 nut
8 peg
9 peg box
10 scroll
11 shoulder
12 tail button
13 tail gut
14 tail piece

Keys and Intervals

1. The first note, the 'doh', of any scale is also called the key note or **tonic**.
   Write the tonic of the major scales that have these key signatures.

2. Finish writing the intervals, adding any accidentals needed.

   perfect 5th   major 7th   major 2nd   perfect 4th   major 6th

3. Name the following intervals.

Transposition

Transposition means to change a melody from one key to another.

Here is a melody in the key of F major.
Transpose it into G major on the staff below.

From F to G is up one tone. First write the new key signature.
Then copy the melody moving every note up one tone.
When you have finished, play both tunes. Do they sound the same?

B♭ Major Scale

B♭ major has two flats: B♭ and E♭. It can be played in two places on the violin, the lower octave starting on the G string, and the upper octave starting where the lower octave ends.

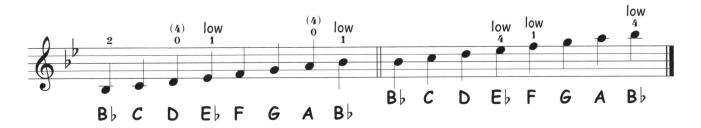

B♭ Major Arpeggio

Sailor's Hornpipe

Traditional English
Folk Dance

This Israeli folk dance is in G minor. It is the relative minor to B♭ major so also has two flats. Place your fingers carefully to play in tune, especially when there are flat notes and sharp notes next to each other.

Hava Nagela

Traditional Jewish

Another New Note: G♯ on the D String

G♯ is a semitone higher than G. Play this note by extending your third finger one semitone further up the string than its usual position.

Twinkle: Starting on the First Finger

A Major Scale

A major has three sharps: F♯, C♯ and G♯.
The lower octave uses the 'high 3' finger pattern.
The upper octave uses the '1-23' pattern starting on open A string.

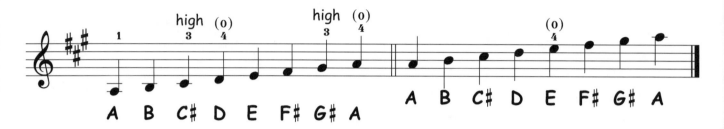

A B C♯ D E F♯ G♯ A   A B C♯ D E F♯ G♯ A

A Major Arpeggio

Come, Follow

This is a **round**, the players starting four bars apart.

Hilton

Challenge
Play this round without
using any open strings.

John Hilton (1599-1657) is a less well
known English composer. He was an organist,
so he mainly wrote music for the church. He
also collected and composed rounds.

A **chorale** is a hymn sung by a choir. It is not known who wrote the original 'St Anthony Chorale', but Haydn used the tune in music he wrote for a military band. Later, in 1873 another composer, Johannes Brahms used the same tune for orchestral music, which he called 'Variations on a Theme by Haydn'.

St Anthony Chorale

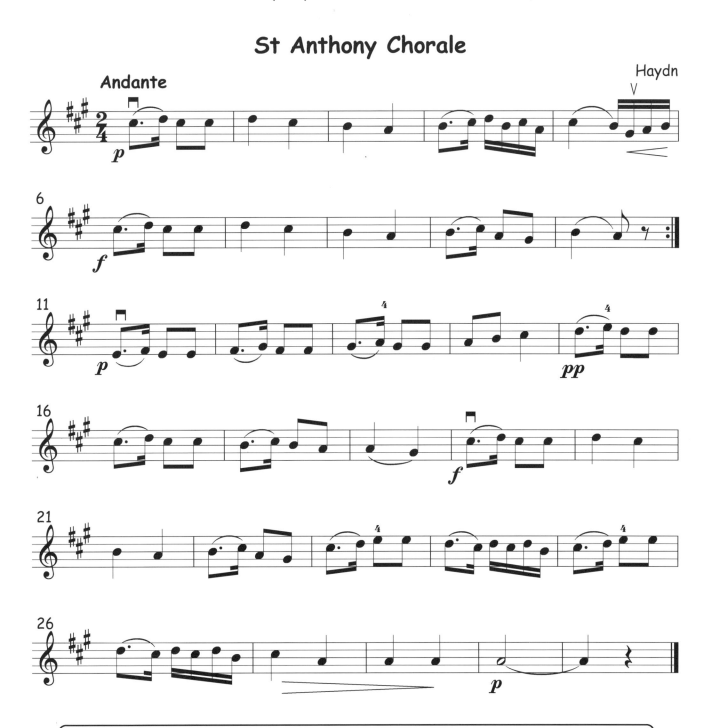

Franz Joseph Haydn (1732-1809) was born in Rohau, a tiny Austrian village, where his father was a wheelwright. At eight years of age he started his musical life as a choirboy in the cathedral in Vienna. He studied singing, harpsichord and violin. He later became musical director to the Prince of Esterhazy, a wealthy and powerful nobleman. He was a prolific composer, writing one hundred and four symphonies and many other works for instrumentalists and singers.

Bow Tricks: Bowing Variations

Abbreviations in music: a single note can be turned into repeated notes of a smaller value by means of a line or lines drawn through the stem of the note. One line turns a crotchet into quavers; two lines into semiquavers. Three lines indicates tremolo.

Tremolo is the Italian word for 'trembling'. Play as many repeated notes as possible for the duration of the note. This is best done with very short bows near the tip.

Study in A

A. Akerman

Variations

Quavers: play each note twice.

1

Triplet quavers: play each note three times.

2

Semiquavers: play each note four times.

3

Tremolo: play as many notes as you can for each beat.

4

Decode the Secret Message

First find the number then the letter to lead you to the message!

1	2	3	4	5	6	7	8	9	10	11
c	s	i	u	m	d	y	o	r	f	g

How many...?

		Number	=	Letter
1	lines in a stave			
2	strings on a violin			
3	semitones in a tone			
4	crotchets in a dotted minim			
5	flats in F major scale			
6	notes in a triplet			
7	sharps in D major scale			
8	Gs in 'Rigaudon' on page 4 without the 'da capo'.			
9	notes in a one octave scale			
10	quavers in a bar of 4/4 time			
11	dohs in 'Twinkle, Twinkle'			
12	black notes on the piano in 2 octaves			
13	semiquavers in a minim			
14	beats in three bars of triple time			
15	alphabet names of the notes			
16	crotchets in two semibreves			
17	beats in simple quadruple time			

Answer:_____

Cantata means 'a sung piece'. It is a musical work for voices with orchestral accompaniment, rather like an opera or musical, but without scenery or action. In olden times it was a story set to music for entertainment or education. This was long before the invention of radio and television.

When playing in the key of D major remember to play C♯, the 'high 3' finger pattern, on the G string.

Now Let Us to the Bagpipe Sound

(from the 'Peasant Cantata')

Johann Sebastian Bach (1685-1750) was the most distinguished of a long line of musicians. As the musical director of St. Thomas's Church and School at Leipzig in Germany, he was responsible for weekly church services, the orchestra, choir and teaching. In those days there was no local music shop, so he wrote everything for himself. He was the father of twenty children, several of whom became famous musicians.

Now Let Us to the Bagpipe Sound

(from the 'Peasant Cantata')

Harmony Part

Nobody knows how old the tune of **Greensleeves** really is. It has been popular for at least 400 years. Many different words have been set to this tune such as the Christmas carol 'What Child is This'. One of the earliest references to Greensleeves was in a play called 'The Merry Wives of Windsor' written by Shakespeare and first published in 1602. There are numerous different versions of the tune. This is one commonly heard nowadays.

Greensleeves

Moderato   16th Century English Air

Find the Composers

Arbeau	Hook
Bach	Lully
Charpentier	Mendelssohn
Couperin	Mozart
Dvorak	Purcell
Gossec	Schubert
Grieg	Tchaikovsky
Handel	Vivaldi
Haydn	Weber

```
T C H A I K O V S K Y
S S C O U P E R I N A
C H A R P E N T I E R
H D B P U H E G S I E
U V A T R A Z O M G B
B O R H C N Y S H R E
E R B A E D L S O I W
R A E Y L E L E O E S
T K A D L L U C K G O
R F U N I D L A V I V
M E N D E L S S O H N
```

50

Before beginning this piece, roll the bow into the palm of your hand and extend your first finger ready for playing **pizzicato**. You may like to balance your hand by placing your thumb on the corner of the fingerboard. Pluck the string over the fingerboard, not where you bow.

Arco means use the bow. During the rest in bar 8, quickly resume your bow hold.

Russian Gypsy Folk Song

Musical Crossword

Clues across

- 4 Soft
- 5 Cut short, detached
- 9 Musical work for choir
- 12 End or finish
- 13 Smoothly
- 15 Gradually faster
- 17 A 17th century stately dance
- 18 Trembling
- 19 Use the bow
- 21 A little faster than andante
- 23 Peacefully, tranquilly

Clues down

- 1 Sweetly
- 2 Loud
- 3 From
- 6 To the
- 7 'Tail' or ending
- 8 Immediately slower
- 10 Lively and fast
- 11 Little by little
- 14 'Half' or moderately
- 15 Return to former speed
- 16 At an easy pace
- 17 At a moderate pace
- 20 With
- 22 Short for gradually softer

Additional Repertoire

Music through time – 550 years

The styles and forms of music from different periods overlap so names and dates are approximate.

The Renaissance: 1450-1600

The word **Renaissance** means re-birth and is the name given to the time when Europe emerged from the Middle Ages. It was a time of very rapid change in European history.

Europeans regarded Europe as the centre of the known world. Explorers were sailing off into the unknown to find new lands. Scientists were making new discoveries about nature and the universe. At this time of great learning, the study of music was important for educated people.

Education was provided mainly by the Christian church, so all learning had a religious basis. Most music written at this time was composed for the church. Folk music was also popular among ordinary people, but this music was not usually written down, rather passed on by ear from person to person.

A **pavan** is a 16th century slow dance usually performed at weddings or solemn feasts. This one was first printed in 1589 in a book of French dances by Thoinot Arbeau.

Pavan

The **music notation** that we use was developed at this time in Italy. That is why Italian words are still widely used today to describe how music is to be played.

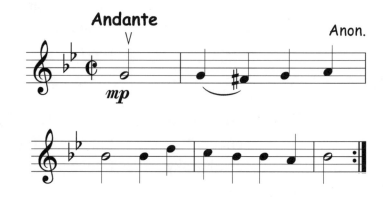

The **invention of printing** at this time helped the spread of learning and widened the circulation of music.

Musicians were employed by the church and at royal courts. At a time when there was no radio, television or recorded music of any kind, musicians provided music for religious festivals, royal occasions, entertainment and dancing.
Thomas Morley (1557-1603) was the organist at St. Paul's Cathedral, London.

Now is the Month of Maying

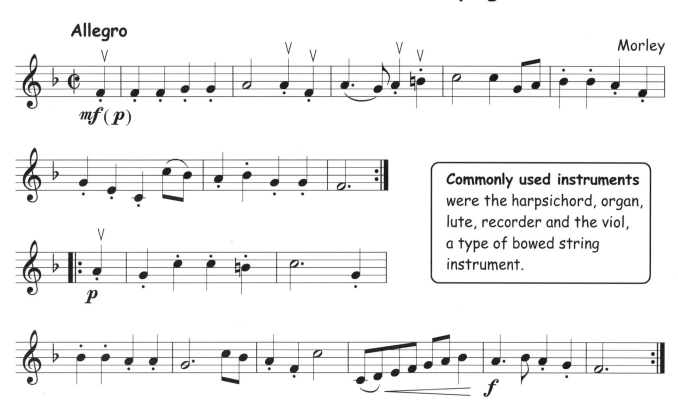

Commonly used instruments were the harpsichord, organ, lute, recorder and the viol, a type of bowed string instrument.

Some interesting dates
1465 The first printed music.
1492 Christopher Columbus discovered the West Indies.
1520 Chocolate and coffee reached Europe.
1540 Copernicus was the first to state that the earth goes around the sun.
1577 Francis Drake sailed around the world.

Other music in this book from Renaissance times:
Page 52   Greensleeves.....Anon.

The Baroque Era: 1600-1750

During the **Baroque** period, buildings and all forms of art were highly decorated and elaborate. It was a time of great scientific discovery.

Jean-Baptiste Lully (1632-1687) was born into a poor family in Florence, Italy where he learnt to play the guitar and violin. When he was 14 years old, a wealthy gentleman was so impressed by his playing that he took Lully to Paris. Lully became composer of dance music in the court of King Louis XIV.

A **gavotte** is a slow and stately dance that was very popular in the French courts. It has four beats in each bar and starts on the third beat.

Gavotte

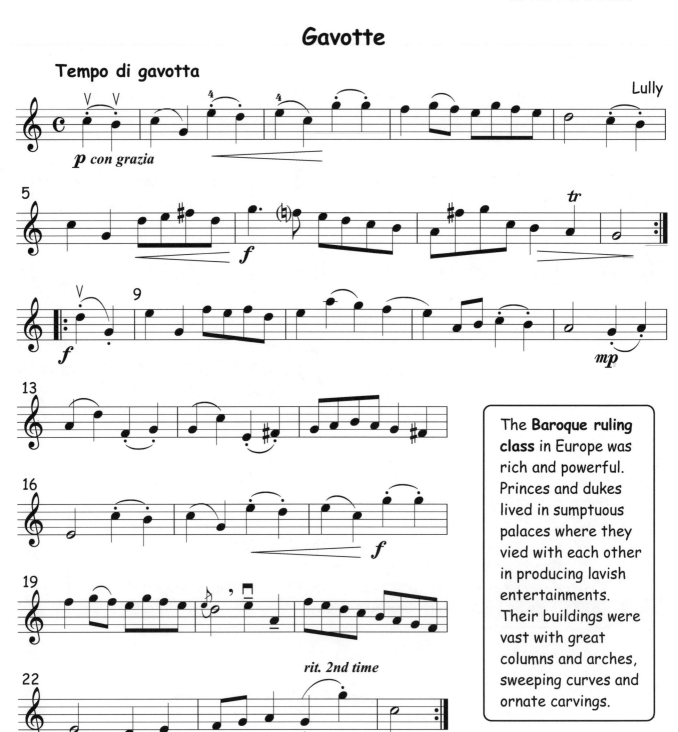

The **Baroque ruling class** in Europe was rich and powerful. Princes and dukes lived in sumptuous palaces where they vied with each other in producing lavish entertainments. Their buildings were vast with great columns and arches, sweeping curves and ornate carvings.

Prelude from 'Te Deum'

Allegro

Charpentier

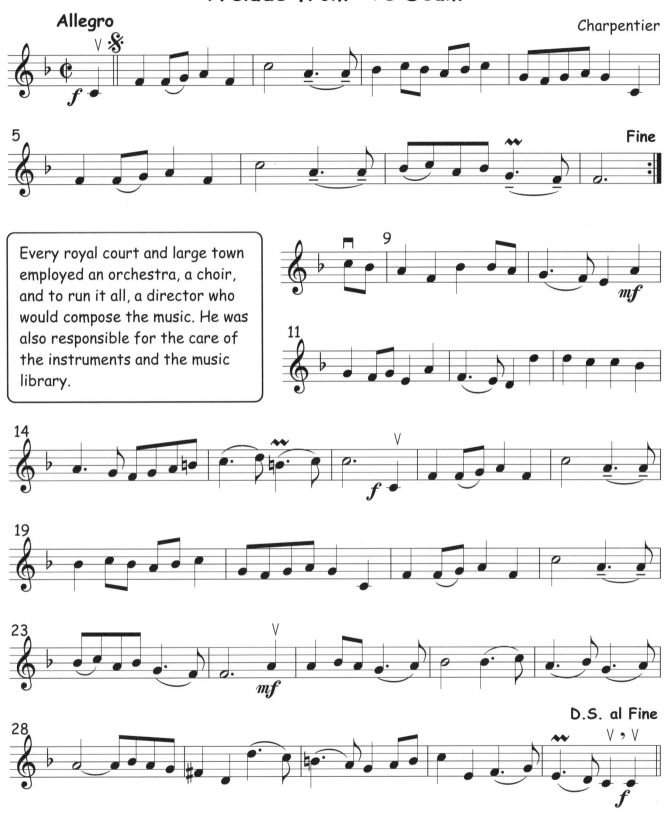

Every royal court and large town employed an orchestra, a choir, and to run it all, a director who would compose the music. He was also responsible for the care of the instruments and the music library.

Churches had music directors to provide music for religious occasions, train the choirboys, and teach in the church school.
Marc-Antoine Charpentier (1643-1704) wrote music for the Dauphin's (the king's heir) private chapel in Paris.

Antonio Vivaldi (1678-1741) was a priest in Venice. He also taught at a famous music school for girls. He wrote this well-known melody as part of a violin concerto called 'The Four Seasons'.

The **violin, viola,** and **cello** family emerged at this time to become the leading musical instruments. The **Amati, Guarneri** and **Stradivari** families from northern Italy were the most important violin makers for several generations.

The Arrival of Spring

Some interesting dates

1639 The world's first printing press.

1665 The Great Plague.

1666 The Great Fire of London.

1666 Antonio Stradivari labelled his first violin.

1709 The invention of the pianoforte by Bartolemeo Christofori.

George Frideric Handel (1685-1759) was born in Germany and played the organ, harpsichord, violin and oboe. He spent three years in Italy performing, studying and composing. On returning home in 1710, he became director of music to the Elector of Hanover. Later that year Handel went to England where he was to spend the rest of his life. This march is from one of his many operas.

March from 'Scipio'

Maestoso

Handel

The Earl of Sandwich invented the sandwich in 1762 when he wanted a quick snack whilst playing cards. He ordered his servant to bring him two slices of bread with a slice of roast beef in between.

Other music in this book from the Baroque era:

The Classical Era: 1750-1820

The term classical is sometimes confusing because it has different meanings. Many people take classical music to mean any music that is not folk, jazz or popular. **Classical** refers to a time in history when music emphasised the beauty of logical form. It was very tuneful and also expressed feelings and emotions.

Theme from Symphony No. 94: 'Surprise' Symphony

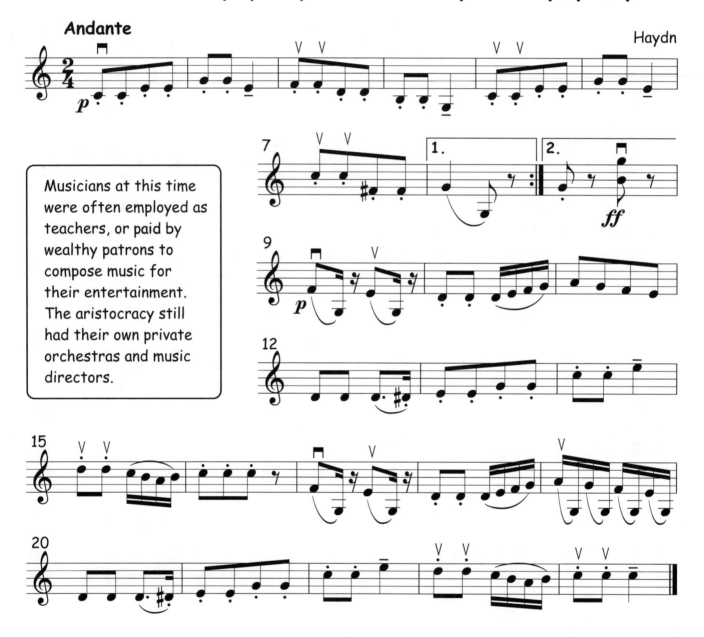

Musicians at this time were often employed as teachers, or paid by wealthy patrons to compose music for their entertainment. The aristocracy still had their own private orchestras and music directors.

The 'Surprise' Symphony was so called because of a sudden loud drumstroke in the middle of a quiet section of music. Haydn thought it would be fun to wake up any old ladies who fell asleep in his concerts!

The strings became the principal orchestral instruments with woodwind, brass and percussion providing contrasting sounds.

François-Joseph Gossec (1734-1829) was a conductor, concert manager and professor of composition at the Paris Conservatoire.

Tambourin is the name of an old French dance in which a percussion instrument called the tambour or tambourine was generally used.

Tambourin

Music at this time was more accessible to the middle classes. Many concert halls were built and people attended the opera or orchestral concerts as people go to the cinema today.

Music had by this time become more complex. The Classical orchestra was far bigger than a Baroque ensemble. Many different instruments were combined to produce a great variety of sounds.

Wolfgang Amadeus Mozart (1756-1791) was born in Salzburg, Austria. He was a brilliant musician who began composing music at five years of age. As a child he travelled through Europe with his father and sister performing on the violin and harpsichord in the royal courts.

Duet

Allegro

Mozart

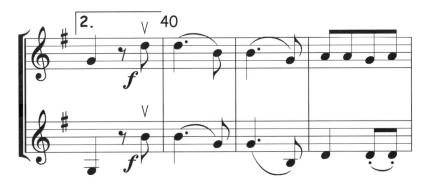

Mozart led the way in composing music for the **clarinet**. It had just evolved by this time from an earlier instrument, the chalumeau. His liking for and use of the clarinet helped it become part of every orchestra. Advances in technology helped the development of other instruments such as the flute, which, originally wood, was now made out of metal.

Some interesting dates
1755 Samuel Johnson wrote the first dictionary of the English language.
1769 James Cook came to Australia.
1776 America became independent from Great Britain.
1812 Napoleon invaded Moscow but was defeated by the Russian winter.

The Romantic Movement: 1820-1900

The **'Romantic'** composers expressed feelings and emotions more intensely than in Classical times. This development in music was mirrored in the paintings and literature of the time. The Romantics loved fantasy and wrote many pieces of music to tell imaginative stories through sound. 'Peer Gynt' by Edvard Grieg (1843-1907) is an example. Music that sets out to tell a story or paint a picture is called **program music**.

Entr'acte from 'Rosamunde'

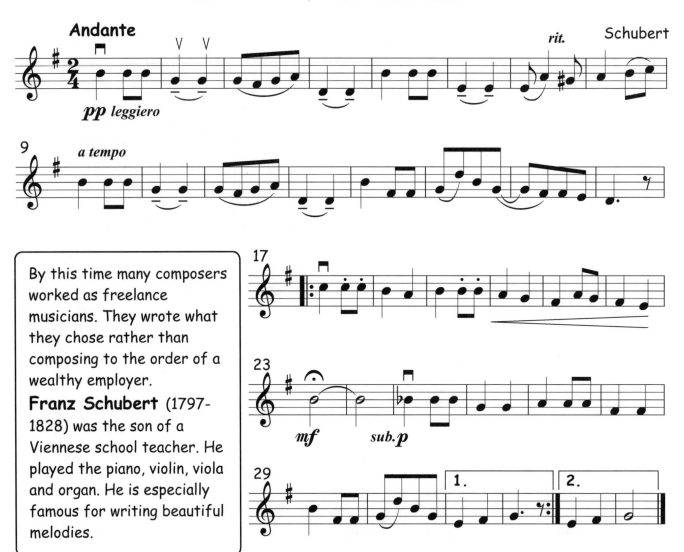

By this time many composers worked as freelance musicians. They wrote what they chose rather than composing to the order of a wealthy employer.

Franz Schubert (1797-1828) was the son of a Viennese school teacher. He played the piano, violin, viola and organ. He is especially famous for writing beautiful melodies.

Entr'acte is a French word meaning 'between acts'. This piece of music was originally written to be performed between the acts of the ballet 'Rosamunde'.

Other music in this book dating from the Romantic movement:

Peter Ilyich Tchaikovsky (1840-1893), a Russian composer, was the first professor of harmony at the newly established Moscow Conservatory of Music. Of his many well-known compositions, the ballet 'Swan Lake' is a special favourite. He wrote it for the Imperial Ballet in St. Petersburg.

Dance of the Cygnets

(From 'Swan Lake')

Tchaikovsky

Orchestras became even larger with a great variety of wind and brass instruments as well as a large string section. Compositions for small groups of musicians were very popular. Music of this type was called **chamber music**, from the French word 'chambre' which means room. One chamber group is the string quartet, which consists of two violins, a viola and a cello.

Nationalism in Music

Nationalism was an extension of the Romantic movement. Composers endeavoured to write music, often based on folk music, that reflected the culture and landscape of their own country. For example, the music of **Antonin Dvorak** (1841-1904) is Czechoslovakian in character, while **Edvard Grieg's** music reflects the folk tunes and tales of Norway.

Slavonic Dance

Norwegian Dance

Some interesting dates

1833 The British Factory Act made it illegal to employ children under nine.

1867-1877 Many new inventions included the domestic sewing machine, typewriter, telephone, record player, Cola drinks, jeans, car and breakfast cereal.

1846 Adolphe Sax invented the saxophone.

The Twentieth Century

The twentieth century was a time of experimentation in musical styles involving the development of recorded music, electronic music, jazz and many other popular idioms. Composers often used discords: notes that when combined, jar or seem to disagree. There were more changes of time and key signature within a piece and rhythms became more complex.

Peter Warlock (1894-1930) was an English composer. When he wrote books about music he used his real name, Philip Heseltine.

Composers sometimes used the tunes of olden times to form the basis of their works. 'Capriol Suite' uses six of Arbeau's Renaissance French dance tunes (including the 'Pavan' on page 54). Warlock arranged these for string orchestra.

Basse Dance

(From 'Capriol Suite')

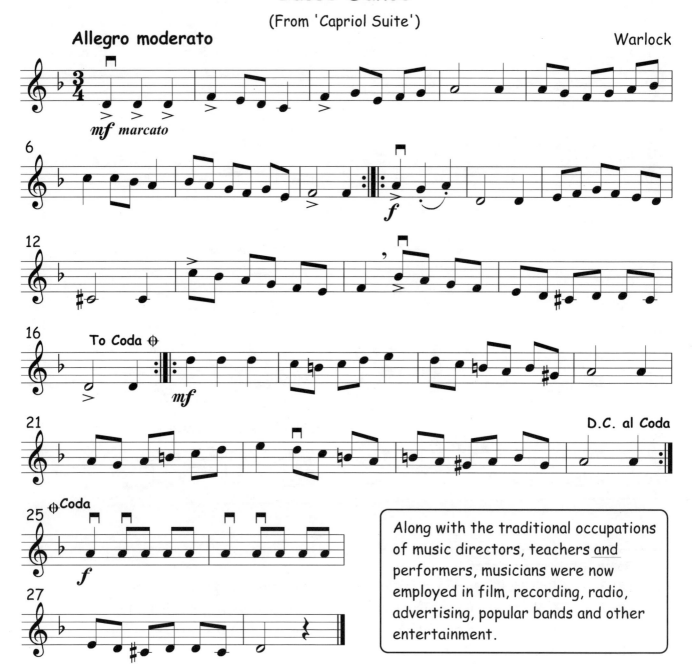

Along with the traditional occupations of music directors, teachers and performers, musicians were now employed in film, recording, radio, advertising, popular bands and other entertainment.

Syncopation: the normal accent is shifted to a beat that is not usually accented.

Ragtime: 'ragged rhythm', was a popular early type of jazz in America, in the 1890s and early 1900s. Pianists imitated the jangling sound of the banjo. It has a strongly syncopated rhythm over a steady oom-pah bass. A well-known rag, 'The Entertainer' by American composer Scott Joplin, was made popular by the movie 'The Sting'.

A Piece of Rag

A. Akerman

Italian Words and Music Signs

A tempo..................................... return to former speed
Accelerando, accel..................... gradually getting faster
Adagio.. slowly
Al .... to the
Allegro.. lively and fast
Andante...................................... at an easy pace
Andantino................................... at a moderate pace, (usually) a little faster than andante
Arco.. with the bow
Cantabile, cantab. .... in a singing style
Coda .... 'tail' or ending
Con .... with
Crescendo, cresc........................ gradually louder
Da Capo, D.C.............................. from the beginning
Dal Segno, D.S........................... from the sign
Decrescendo, decresc. .... gradually softer
Di... of, by
Diminuendo, dim. .... gradually softer
Dolce.. sweetly, gently
E... and
Fermata...................................... pause
Fine .... (the) end, finish
Forte, *f*.................................... loud
Fortissimo, *ff*........................... very loud
Grazioso .... gracefully
Largo.. broad, slow and stately
Leggiero .... lightly
Legato... smoothly
Maestoso.................................... majestic
Mezzo, *m* .... moderately (in Italian, really means half)
Minuetto .... minuet, a dance in triple time
Moderato.................................... at a moderate speed
Pianissimo, *pp*.......................... very soft
Piano, *p*.................................... soft
Pizzicato, pizz............................. plucked
Poco... a little
Poco a poco .... little by little
Rallentando, rall. .... gradually getting slower
Ritardando, ritard. .... gradually getting slower
Ritenuto, riten., rit..................... immediately slower, held back
Simile.. similarly, in the same way
Spiritoso .... spirited, with spirit, energy
Staccato .... cut short, detached
Subito, sub. .... immediately
Tempo... pace, time
Tenuto .... held
Tranquillo.................................... peacefully, tranquilly
Tremolo....................................... trembling
Vivo, Vivace .... lively